TRUTHS FOR LIFE

JIM BERG

WHEN
TROUBLE
COMES

STUDY GUIDE

BJU PRESS
GREENVILLE, SOUTH CAROLINA

Cover image by PhotoDisc, Inc.

All Scripture is quoted from the Authorized King James Version.

When Trouble Comes
Jim Berg

Design by Brannon McAllister
Composition by Melissa Matos

© 2004 by BJU Press
Greenville, South Carolina 29614

ISBN 1-57924-971-X

15   14   13   12   11   10   9   8   7   6   5   4   3   2   1

Table of Contents

INTRODUCTION

Wise people prepare for any crisis they see on the horizon.

Coastal dwellers in my home state of South Carolina quickly move into an "emergency preparedness" mode when they are informed that a hurricane is brewing in the Atlantic and will make landfall within a few days or hours.

They board up windows, move outdoor furniture inside, remove valuables, and work feverishly until the last possible moment when they have to vacate the dwelling themselves and move to safety further inland.

Though everyone within hurricane-prone regions knows that the potential of a threatening storm exists, not everyone takes the necessary precautions that will preserve as much property and life as possible. Some people are ignorant of how best to prepare for a hurricane. Some are lazy; others are "eternally optimistic" and never quite grasp the gravity of the danger. The losses are great for everyone, but especially for those who did not take reasonable measures to protect themselves from the ravishes of the storm.

We must recognize that as long as we live on this sin-cursed planet with sinful people, we are going to encounter many storms. Wise people will prepare for those storms and will be able to weather them without great losses and, more importantly, without damage to the name and reputation of the God they claim to serve.

This study is very much like a "survival manual" for the times of trouble, which inevitably will hit our lives. May this brief study better equip you to handle the storms of life to the glory of God.

Week 1

THE DANGER

| The greatest danger is always the flesh. |

DAY 1

☑ TAKE TIME TO READ THE TEXT

     Read chapter 1, pages 1-10, of WTC.[1]

❑ TAKE TIME TO REFLECT UPON THE TRUTH

1. In the blanks below write the two most significant statements in today's reading assignment. Be prepared to discuss why the statements you chose were significant to you.

    a. *P6 It is important that we accurately diagnose our trouble & respond correctly*
      P8 Scriptural joy ... Is a direct result of increased fellowship with God

---

[1]WTC refers to the text, *When Trouble Comes.*

b. p9 Jesus not only feels the afflictions we experience but He is ready to help me in my time of need.

2. Review the eleven crisis situations listed on pages 4-6 of WTC. Then list the crisis situations you face right now or suspect you will face within the near future.

My Son Cole is expecting a child he is not married And the mother has decided She wants to be with another man / my job my husbands Role

3. Which crisis situation in the past was the scene of your biggest failure? Why?

The exact Same as Cole engaging in premarital sex This set my life up backwards & led me down a path of many bad decisions

4. Which crisis situation in the past was the scene of your biggest success? Why?

Abortion - God has used that in a powerful way for His Glory touching others at their need

5. The word lust in the verse for this week means simply "strong desire." The context of the word determines whether the strong desire is good or bad. These verses teach that the desires of the "flesh"—those generated by our sinful nature—are at war with those things the Spirit of God desires for us. When we indulge in the desires of our sinful flesh, we disobey the Spirit of God and damage our relationship with Jesus Christ.

What strong desires of your flesh—your sinful nature—keep you from walking in a close relationship with Jesus Christ? They can be attitudes, actions, or ambitions.

I have been working hard for a long time maybe thinking I can fix something

6. To "walk in the Spirit" means to listen to the conviction of God's Spirit through His Word and to obey Him. The result is that our "walk," or "lifestyle," reflects godly responses rather than fleshly reactions. Your text says, "[God] does not promise to deliver us from our negative circumstances, but He does promise to deliver us from the wrong responses—the dangers—that will destroy our joy and obscure His glory (I Corinthians 10:13)" (WTC, 9-10).

If you were walking in the Spirit instead of walking after your flesh in the areas you listed in the above question, what would your responses look like?

I would be doing things with Jesus and not be doing things for Jesus I would be walking in more peace & confidence

❏ TAKE TIME TO RENEW YOUR MIND

Memorize Galatians 5:16-17 this week. Review it daily throughout the entire week and be prepared to write it from memory on Day 5.[2]

[16] *This I say then, Walk in the Spirit, and ye shall not fulfil the lust of the flesh.*
[17] *For the flesh lusteth against the Spirit, and the Spirit against the flesh: and these are contrary the one to the other: so that ye cannot do the things that ye would.*

❏ TAKE TIME TO RESPOND TO GOD

To build a relationship with God, you will need to respond to Him about the things you have learned from Him today. Strengthen your prayer time by "PRAYing." Jot down some topics you wish to include in your conversation with God so that you are not speaking without thinking.

---

[2]If you already know Galatians 5:16-17 or wish to memorize additional passsages, consider memorizing I Corinthians 10:13, James 1:12, or James 1:1-8.

Praise: <u>For Salvation, speaking, preccnce</u>

Repent: <u>pride, trying to do my own thing</u>

Ask: <u>For strength to endure, a closer walk, help
to memorize • Know the exact words of God!</u>

- Your text says, "Every test of life—every crisis—has within it a danger
  that we cannot 'escape' if we respond wrongly and an opportunity to
  show how great God is if we respond correctly" (WTC, 2). This week
  ask God to make you increasingly conscious of that truth so that you
  can avoid the dangers of a wrong response and can show something of
  God to others by a correct response.

Yield: <u>This whole situation to God and to</u>
yield in submission to Mack and trust
that God will handle him.

DAY 2

☑TAKE TIME TO READ THE TEXT

Read chapter 2, pages 11-18, of WTC.

❑ TAKE TIME TO REFLECT UPON THE TRUTH

1. In the blanks below write the two most significant statements in today's
    reading assignment. Be prepared to discuss why the statements you chose
    were significant to you.

    a.   p 13 Responding in self centered anger
    and bitterness will further alienate ———
    and complicate reconciliation with God
    for ———

    b.   Though other people are responsible for
    the wound I am responsible for
    my reaction to it.

2. The text lists several fleshly ways that Peggy could have reacted to Bill's
    sin with pornography. List several other fleshly responses that she could
    have had.

    made him pay in holding it over his head
    retreated into herself
    treated him like a disease

3. Read Numbers 20:1-13. Check the box when you have finished reading
    the passage. Then answer the following questions from the passage. ☑

a. What was the crisis facing the people of Israel in Numbers 20?

No water

b. Describe their sinful, fleshly response. they were angry and blamed moses & aaron for the situation

c. What crisis did Moses face? Dealing with a million angry thirsty people they had a real need to line

d. Describe Moses' sinful, fleshly response. He struck the rock instead of speaking to it

e. How did Moses' sinful, fleshly response complicate an already bad situation? It brought a punishment on Him & Aaron /

f. What might Moses have been able to teach the people about God had he responded correctly? God is the provider not man

g. According to Numbers 20:12 what did God say was at the root of Moses' sinful response? trust

❏ TAKE TIME TO RENEW YOUR MIND

Memorize Galatians 5:16-17 this week.

❏ TAKE TIME TO RESPOND TO GOD

To build a relationship with God, you will need to respond to Him about the things you have learned from Him today. Strengthen your prayer time by "PRAYing." Jot down some topics you wish to include in your conversation with God so that you are not speaking without thinking.

<u>P</u>raise: _You God for your word_

<u>R</u>epent: _of my reactions in flesh_

<u>A</u>sk: _for your glorious presence to help me and guide me_

- Your text says, "Every test of life—every crisis—has within it a danger that we cannot 'escape' if we respond wrongly and an opportunity to show how great God is if we respond correctly" (WTC, 2). This week ask God to make you increasingly conscious of that truth so that you can avoid the dangers of a wrong response and can show something of God to others by a correct response.

<u>Y</u>ield: _my stubborn will_

This I say then; walk in the Spirit and ye shall not fulfil the lust of the flesh

For the flesh lusteth against the Spirit and the Spirit against the flesh

DAY 3

☑ TAKE TIME TO REFLECT UPON THE TRUTH

1. Read II Kings 5:1-14. Check the box when you have finished reading the passage. Then answer the following questions from the passage. ☑

    a. What physical crisis was Naaman facing? __leprosy__

    _____

    b. First Peter 5:5 describes a spiritual crisis we all face. How does I Peter 5:5 also describe Naaman's most important crisis—his spiritual

    need? __Humility__

    _____

    _____

2. According to I Peter 5:5 what is God's solution to our stubborn pride and the means whereby we can obtain God's grace—His divine help?

    __Submit__

    _____

3. In what crises of life are you most prone to react stubbornly? Think of those areas where God, others, and your own conscience accuse you of being stubbornly self-centered. Here are some examples: I am stubborn when . . .

    • My spouse suggests a better way to do something. I'd rather do it my own way.

    • My parents set a curfew for me. I think that I am old enough to set my own schedule.

    • My pastor questions me about the sin battle I have struggled with. I don't like to be held accountable for my life.

List at least five areas of similar stubbornness in your own life.

a. _I want things done my way_

b. _I struggle with being on time_

c. _I like to be noticed for what I do_

d. _I don't pray enough I try to take things into my own hands_

e. _my keep the trust I have built since I couldn't be trusted._

❏ TAKE TIME TO RENEW YOUR MIND

Memorize Galatians 5:16-17 this week.

❏ TAKE TIME TO RESPOND TO GOD

To build a relationship with God, you will need to respond to Him about the things you have learned from Him today. Strengthen your prayer time by "PRAYing." Jot down some topics you wish to include in your conversation with God so that you are not speaking without thinking.

16 So I say walk by the Spirit and you will not gratify the desires of the flesh

Praise: _____

Repent: _____

Ask: _____

- Your text says, "Every test of life—every crisis—has within it a danger that we cannot 'escape' if we respond wrongly and an opportunity to show how great God is if we respond correctly" (WTC, 2). This week ask God to make you increasingly conscious of that truth so that you can avoid the dangers of a wrong response and can show something of God to others by a correct response.

Yield: _____

Day 4

❑ Take Time to Reflect upon the Truth

1. Read Romans 12:17-21. Check the box when you have finished reading the passage. Then answer the following questions from the passage. ❑ Verse 17 tells us that we should never pay back evil for evil. That means that vengeance is never an option when someone wrongs us. Revenge only further "infects the wound." It brings more evil into the situation. We cannot win the war against evil by using evil as a weapon in the conflicts of life. Revenge includes more than fistfights and name-calling. It includes . . .

   - Punishing the offender with the "silent treatment"
   - Gossiping about the offender's faults and failures to others
   - Rebuking the offender in a spirit contrary to Galatians 6:1 and Matthew 7:3-5
      - Giving the offender a good "tongue-lashing" (i.e., using harsh, critical, or insensitive words)
      - Treating the offender with scorn and contempt (i.e., blowing the horn at the car that cut you off in traffic, scowling at the offender as you walk by him)

   When someone wrongs you, in what ways are you tempted to pay back evil for evil? _____

   _____

   _____

2. In Bible times when an enemy was trying to scale the walls of a city, the enemy would often put ladders up the side of the walls in order to climb over them. Those defending the city from the inside would start large bonfires and throw the hot coals over the walls onto the heads of the enemies coming up the ladders. Doing so was very effective in discouraging the enemy.

   This is the picture Paul is alluding to in Romans 12:20, when he says that overcoming evil with good is very effective in winning the war against evil just as throwing hot coals on the heads of the enemies was very effective in holding off the enemy advances.

Bear in mind that Paul is not teaching that we should find some way to hurt the one who has hurt us. We are to find some way to hurt the advance of evil into the situation by overcoming the evil with good. What "good" could Peggy bring into her crisis that would help "overcome [Bill's] evil with good"?

_____

_____

_____

❏ Take Time to Renew Your Mind

Memorize Galatians 5:16-17.

❏ Take Time to Respond to God

To build a relationship with God, you will need to respond to Him about the things you have learned from Him today. Strengthen your prayer time by "PRAYing." Jot down some topics you wish to include in your conversation with God so that you are not speaking without thinking.

Praise: _____

Repent: _____

Ask: _____

_____

- Your text says, "Every test of life—every crisis—has within it a danger that we cannot 'escape' if we respond wrongly and an opportunity to show how great God is if we respond correctly" (WTC, 2). This week ask God to make you increasingly conscious of that truth so that you can avoid the dangers of a wrong response and can show something of God to others by a correct response.

Yield: _____

DAY 5

❏ TAKE TIME TO REFLECT UPON THE TRUTH

1. Read James 3:1-18. Check the box when you have finished reading the
    passage. Then answer the following questions from the passage. ❏
    This passage contrasts godly responses with fleshly responses, especially as
    they pertain to the use of our tongue.

2. What characteristics of fleshly responses are given in the following verses?

    *   Verse 5 _____

    *   Verse 6 _____

    *   Verse 8 _____

    *   Verse 9 _____

    *   Verse 10 _____

    *   Verse 14 _____

    *   Verse 16 _____

3. According to James 3:15 what is the source of the fleshly responses you
    just studied in the verses listed above? _____

    _____

4. What characteristics of spiritual responses are given in the following
    verses?

    *   Verse 9 _____

    *   Verse 13 _____

    _____

    *   Verse 17 _____

    _____

    _____

- Verse 18 _____

_____

❏ TAKE TIME TO RENEW YOUR MIND

Write Galatians 5:16-17 from memory.

_____

_____

_____

_____

_____

_____

_____

❏ TAKE TIME TO RESPOND TO GOD

To build a relationship with God, you will need to respond to Him about the things you have learned from Him today. Strengthen your prayer time by "PRAYing." Jot down some topics you wish to include in your conversation with God so that you are not speaking without thinking.

Praise: _____

Repent: _____

Ask: _____

_____

- Your text says, "Every test of life—every crisis—has within it a danger that we cannot 'escape' if we respond wrongly and an opportunity to show how great God is if we respond correctly" (WTC, 2). This week ask God to make you increasingly conscious of that truth so that you can avoid the dangers of a wrong response and can show something of God to others by a correct response.

Yield: _____

❏ TAKE TIME TO REORDER YOUR LIFE

Considering this week's reflections, write below anything you need to begin to do differently in your life. List as well the person whom you will ask to hold you accountable for these changes.

_____

_____

_____

_____

Week 2

THE DELIVERANCE

The gospel is always the answer.

DAY 1

❏ TAKE TIME TO READ THE TEXT

> Read chapter 3, pages 19-27, of WTC.

❏ TAKE TIME TO REFLECT UPON THE TRUTH

1. In the blanks below write the two most significant statements in today's reading assignment. Be prepared to discuss why the statements you chose were significant to you.

   a. _____

   _____

   _____

   _____

   _____

b. _____

_____

_____

_____

_____

2. According to your reading in WTC, what is the biggest crisis a man can face?

_____

3. How would you answer the following question presented in your reading for today: "If you were to die today from a terminal illness or in some tragic accident and you were to stand before God, how would you answer God when He asked you this question: 'Why should I let you into My heaven?'" (WTC, 21).

_____

_____

_____

4. Some people feel that God should let them into heaven because they have lived sacrificial lives or have lived by a high moral standard. What does Titus 3:5 say about the ability of these "works of righteousness" to gain us entrance into heaven?

_____

_____

5. Eternal life is not a reward for living a good life since all men are sinners and are sentenced to eternal death for their sin according to Romans 3:23 and Romans 6:23. What does I John 5:11-12 say we must have to be assured that we have eternal life?

_____

6. According to Romans 10:9-10, what is required for a man to be able to have eternal salvation?

_____

7. Can you confidently say that you have eternal life because you have trusted Jesus Christ as your personal sin substitute and you now have a personal relationship with Him because His Spirit lives in you? _____

❑ TAKE TIME TO RENEW YOUR MIND

> Memorize Romans 8:31-32 this week. Review it daily throughout the entire week and be prepared to write it from memory on Day 5.[1]
>
> *31 What shall we then say to these things? If God be for us, who can be against us? 32 He that spared not his own Son, but delivered him up for us all, how shall he not with him also freely give us all things?*

❑ TAKE TIME TO RESPOND TO GOD

> To build a relationship with God, you will need to respond to Him about the things you have learned from Him today. Strengthen your prayer time by "PRAYing." Jot down some topics you wish to include in your conversation with God so that you are not speaking without thinking.

Praise: _____

Repent: _____

Ask: _____

_____

- If you do not have a personal relationship with Jesus Christ, you can have that today by praying a prayer to Him like the one written out for you on page 26 of WTC.
- If you are already a born-again believer, thank God that He sent someone to you with the good news that Jesus Christ came to seek and to save that which was lost—and that He found you!

Yield: _____

---

[1]If you already know Romans 8:31-32 or wish to memorize additional passsages, consider memorizing Matthew 16:24-26, Titus 2:11-12, or Romans 8:35-39.

DAY 2

❑ TAKE TIME TO READ THE TEXT

Read chapter 4, pages 29-38, of WTC.

❑ TAKE TIME TO REFLECT UPON THE TRUTH

1. In the blanks below write the two most significant statements in today's reading assignment. Be prepared to discuss why the statements you chose were significant to you.

    a. _____

    _____

    _____

    _____

    _____

    b. _____

    _____

    _____

    _____

2. In the section entitled "Live the Christian Life the Same Way You Got It," your text said, "The gospel reveals man's condition. . . . The Bible teaches us that we still have within us the bent to live selfishly—to think of ourselves first. This inclination to think of ourselves first seems overwhelming at times—especially if we are in great pain" (WTC, 31). In our study together last week we looked at the danger of this fleshly nature from many angles. We will not expand on it further here, but we must keep in mind this sinful tendency if we are to appreciate that "the gospel reveals God's provision" (WTC, 31).

    God knew that life on a fallen planet would be extremely hard for us. One day He will destroy this earth after transporting all of His redeemed children to be with Him. Until that time He has made some very powerful provisions for us so that we do not have to be consumed by evil when we are in a crisis.

3. Just as Jesus Christ is God's provision for our eternal salvation, He is also our provision when we face temporal trouble. The memory passage for this week, Romans 8:31-32, is very clear about this. Put the truths of these two verses in your own words.

_____

_____

_____

_____

Here is a powerful yet often overlooked comfort for God's people. He loves us! Believers who do not have a God-taught sense of this truth will often feel overwhelmed and alone in their troubled times. We shall look at God's love again in tomorrow's study.

❏ TAKE TIME TO RENEW YOUR MIND

Memorize Romans 8:31-32.

❏ TAKE TIME TO RESPOND TO GOD

To build a relationship with God, you will need to respond to Him about the things you have learned from Him today. Strengthen your prayer time by "PRAYing." Jot down some topics you wish to include in your conversation with God so that you are not speaking without thinking.

Praise: _____

Repent: _____

Ask: _____

_____

- Today ask God to give you a fresh understanding of and appreciation for what it means that He loves you. It will be a major source of stability when the times of pressure come.

Yield: _____

DAY 3

❏ TAKE TIME TO REFLECT UPON THE TRUTH

1. Read Romans 8:35-39. Check the box when you have finished reading the passage. Then answer the following questions from the passage. ❏

2. Why do you think Paul had to remind us about God's love when we are facing trials?

_____

_____

_____

3. Describe a time of difficulty when you were tempted to doubt God's love.

_____

_____

_____

_____

4. In Psalm 18 David is facing a crisis. He is being chased by King Saul, who intends to put David to death. This psalm is David's account of his deliverance. Read Psalm 18:1-19. Check the box when you have finished reading the passage. Then answer the following questions from the passage. ❏

   In verse 19 David gave the reason that the Lord delivered Him. What is that reason?

_____

5. Would you say that the Lord has the same "delight" in you? Explain your answer.

_____

_____

_____

_____

❏ Take Time to Renew Your Mind

Memorize Romans 8:31-32.

❏ Take Time to Respond to God

To build a relationship with God, you will need to respond to Him about the things you have learned from Him today. Strengthen your prayer time by "PRAYing." Jot down some topics you wish to include in your conversation with God so that you are not speaking without thinking.

<u>P</u>raise: _____

<u>R</u>epent: _____

<u>A</u>sk: _____

- Today ask God to give you a fresh understanding of and appreciation for what it means that He loves you. It will be a major source of stability when the times of pressure come.

<u>Y</u>ield: _____

DAY 4

❏ TAKE TIME TO REFLECT UPON THE TRUTH

1. Read Hebrews 11:1-40. Check the box when you have finished reading the passage. Then answer the following questions from the passage. ❏ Hebrews 11 is God's "Hall of Faith." In it He shows us the kind of people who please Him. The chapter lists many familiar Bible heroes—Noah, Abraham, Joseph, and Moses. But it also speaks of a host of nameless "heroes," many of whom lost their lives for their godly testimony.

2. According to Hebrews 11:27 what sustained Moses during his times of difficulty?

_____

3. What application does that have for you?

_____

_____

4. Having "faith" just means that even in the midst of trouble we do not turn our eyes away from God. Some people think that if they can acquire enough of this thing called "faith" they can cash it in to God for the deliverance they want from their problems. Faith, however, is "the gaze of the soul upon a saving God."[2] When we "have faith," we do not let the distractions of our trials cause us to forget God's purposes for us nor His provisions for us during these times. How well do you keep your focus on God's purposes and provisions during times of trouble? Give an example of a time you did focus on God.

_____

_____

_____

5. No one can keep his "gaze . . . upon the saving God" if he is not spending much daily time in the Word of God. God uses the Bible, His inspired Word, to instruct us about Himself and to remind us of our responsibilities to Him. This is the message of Romans 10:17, which says, "so then faith cometh by hearing, and hearing by the word of God." It is

---

[2]A. W. Tozer, *The Pursuit of God* (Camp Hill, Pa.: Christian Publications, 1982), 81.

important that you not miss the direct connection between a believer's ability to handle trials well and the quality of the relationship he has with God through His Word. If you are honest with yourself, what part does the Word of God have in your daily life?

_____

_____

_____

❏ TAKE TIME TO RENEW YOUR MIND

Memorize Romans 8:31-32.

❏ TAKE TIME TO RESPOND TO GOD

To build a relationship with God, you will need to respond to Him about the things you have learned from Him today. Strengthen your prayer time by "PRAYing." Jot down some topics you wish to include in your conversation with God so that you are not speaking without thinking.

Praise: _____

Repent: _____

Ask: _____

_____

- Today ask God to help you see Him more clearly in His Word as you read it and study it every day. Remember that your confidence—your faith—in who God is and what He is like cannot grow without daily, reflective time in the Word.

Yield: _____

DAY 5

❏ TAKE TIME TO REFLECT UPON THE TRUTH

1. Read again Tim Mahler's testimony on pages 33-36 of WTC. Check the box when you have finished the reading. ❏

    What encouraged you most about Tim's testimony? _____

    _____

    _____

2. Read again the prayer on pages 37-38 of WTC. Check the box when you have finished the reading. ❏

    Can you say that this prayer is the testimony of your heart? _____

    If it is not a reality to you at this time, what is keeping you from turning to God in this way?

    _____

    _____

    _____

    _____

    If it is the prayer of your heart, what difference is it making in the way you have handled problems recently?

    _____

    _____

    _____

    _____

    _____

❏ Take Time to Renew Your Mind

Write Romans 8:31-32 from memory.

_____

_____

_____

_____

_____

_____

_____

❏ Take Time to Respond to God

To build a relationship with God, you will need to respond to Him about the things you have learned from Him today. Strengthen your prayer time by "PRAYing." Jot down some topics you wish to include in your conversation with God so that you are not speaking without thinking.

Praise: _____

Repent: _____

Ask: _____

- Today continue to ask God to give you a fresh understanding and appreciation that He loves you enough to deliver you. It will be a major source of stability when the pressure times come.

Yield: _____

❏ Take Time to Reorder Your Life

Considering this week's reflections, write below anything you need to begin to do differently in your life. List as well the person whom you will ask to hold you accountable for these changes.

_____

_____

_____

_____

Week 3

THE DISPLAY

God's glory is always the goal.

DAY 1

❑ TAKE TIME TO READ THE TEXT

Read chapter 5, pages 39-49, of WTC.

❑ TAKE TIME TO REFLECT UPON THE TRUTH

1. In the blanks below write the two most significant statements in today's reading assignment. Be prepared to discuss why the statements you chose were significant to you.

    a. _____

    _____

    _____

    _____

    _____

    b. _____

    _____

2. The phrase "glorifying God" means that we show God to be first in some way through our decisions. He is first in priority and importance. No one deserves as much honor and respect as the Creator of all things. He is also first in all of His attributes. No one has more love, more patience, more power, more wisdom, more faithfulness, and more compassion than the Creator God of the Bible.

Those of us who have tasted His wonderful goodness and have seen His overwhelming greatness desire to give Him the credit He deserves in every decision we make. This is what Paul meant when he said, "Whether therefore ye eat, or drink, or whatsoever ye do, do all to the glory of God" (I Corinthians 10:31). In other words, no matter what circumstance you find yourself in, make decisions that show that God is first.

If you are honest with yourself, how much does "glorifying God"—making sure that He is shown to be first—matter to you in the daily decisions you make? Rate yourself in the areas listed below, using the following scale.

1-strongly agree 2-agree 3-somewhat agree 4-slightly disagree 5-strongly disagree

___ I daily spend time in God's Word so that by knowing Him better my confidence in Him can grow and I can more easily put Him first.

___ I readily turn to God in prayer when I face troubled times because if I do not quickly submit to Him and His ways in my crisis, I will eventually make a fleshly response.

___ I want others to know that God is first, and I regularly witness of His salvation to those around me who are lost.

___ I show that God is first through the use of my money and time. I do not squander them on my own interests but consciously seek to advance His kingdom by the way I use these resources.

___ When I receive undeserved wrong from someone else, I make it my primary goal to reach that person's heart so that his relationship with me and with God can be restored.

___ I am conscious that my personal integrity and God's reputation are at stake in the manner in which I carry out my responsibilities at my employment and at home. I, therefore, seek to maintain a Christian testimony that is above reproach in these areas.

___ I know that to walk in the Spirit I must not "make any provision for the flesh" in my life. Therefore, I am very cautious about the amount and the kinds of entertainment and recreation I pursue.

How would you summarize your overall concern for the glory of God, based upon your responses to these biblical responsibilities? _____

_____

_____

_____

❏ Take Time to Renew Your Mind

Memorize Matthew 5:16 this week. Review it daily throughout the entire week and be prepared to write it from memory on Day 5.[1]

Let your light so shine before men, that they may see your good works, and glorify your Father which is in heaven.

❏ Take Time to Respond to God

To build a relationship with God, you will need to respond to Him about the things you have learned from Him today. Strengthen your prayer time by "PRAYing." Jot down some topics you wish to include in your conversation with God so that you are not speaking without thinking.

Praise: _____

Repent: _____

Ask: _____

_____

- Today ask God to make you sensitive to the events in your daily life that give you the opportunity to show that God is first. Also ask Him for the grace to deny yourself in those situations so that you do not put yourself first.

Yield: _____

---

[1]If you already know Matthew 5:16 or wish to memorize additional passsages, consider memorizing I Corinthians 6:19-20, I Corinthians 10:31, or II Corinthians 4:5-11.

DAY 2

❏ TAKE TIME TO REFLECT UPON THE TRUTH

1. Read Daniel 3:1-30. Check the box when you have finished reading the passage. Then answer the following questions from the passage. ❏

2. What choices did the Hebrews make that showed that God was first?

_____

_____

_____

3. What other choices could they have made that would have shown they were thinking of themselves first?

_____

_____

_____

4. What effect did their choice to show that God is first have on other people?

_____

_____

_____

5. List at least five choices you have faced within the past two days that showed that either God was first or you were first in your life.

a. _____

_____

b. _____

_____

c. _____

_____

d. _____

_____

e. _____

_____

TAKE TIME TO RENEW YOUR MIND

Memorize Matthew 5:16.

❏ TAKE TIME TO RESPOND TO GOD

To build a relationship with God, you will need to respond to Him about the things you have learned from Him today. Strengthen your prayer time by "PRAYing." Jot down some topics you wish to include in your conversation with God so that you are not speaking without thinking.

Praise: _____

Repent: _____

Ask: _____

_____

- Today continue to ask God to make you sensitive to the events in your daily life that give you the opportunity to show that God is first. Also ask Him for the grace to deny yourself in those situations so that you do not put yourself first.

Yield: _____

DAY 3

❏ TAKE TIME TO READ THE TEXT

Read chapter 6, pages 51-59, of WTC.

❏ TAKE TIME TO REFLECT UPON THE TRUTH

1. In the blanks below write the two most significant statements in today's reading assignment. Be prepared to discuss why the statements you chose were significant to you.

a. _____

_____

_____

_____

b. _____

_____

_____

_____

2. Your reading for today lists two reasons people say "I have a hard time trusting God." What are those two reasons?

a. _____

_____

_____

b. _____

_____

_____

3. According to your reading today why could we say that every decision is a
    trust decision?

    _____

    _____

    _____

❏ Take Time to Renew Your Mind

>   Memorize Matthew 5:16.

❏ Take Time to Respond to God

>   To build a relationship with God, you will need to respond to Him
>   about the things you have learned from Him today. Strengthen your prayer
>   time by "PRAYing." Jot down some topics you wish to include in your
>   conversation with God so that you are not speaking without thinking.

Praise: _____

Repent: _____

Ask: _____

    _____

*   Today ask God to make you more and more aware that your every
    decision reveals who it is you trust most—God or yourself. Be sure to
    ask forgiveness for those decisions that revealed you trusted yourself
    most. Those decisions glorified you—put you first and robbed God of
    His glory.

Yield: _____

DAY 4

❏ TAKE TIME TO REFLECT UPON THE TRUTH

1. Read II Chronicles 14:1-15. Check the box when you have finished reading the passage. Then answer the following question from the passage. ❏

2. Asa was the king of Judah, and though his kingdom enjoyed ten years of relative peace, he eventually faced a formidable foe of a million Ethiopians. What choices did Asa make, both in his ten years of peace and in his preparation for battle, that showed he was thoroughly convinced that showing God to be first was his primary mission as king? List several.

_____

_____

_____

_____

_____

3. Read II Chronicles 16:1-10. Check the box when you have finished reading the passage. Then answer the following question from the passage. ❏

4. Asa was faced again with a time of trouble. This time an army from the Northern Kingdom, Israel, invaded the Southern Kingdom, Judah. What choices did Asa make this time that revealed he was no longer putting God first in his thinking?

_____

_____

_____

_____

_____

❏ Take Time to Renew Your Mind

Memorize Matthew 5:16.

❏ Take Time to Respond to God

To build a relationship with God, you will need to respond to Him about the things you have learned from Him today. Strengthen your prayer time by "PRAYing." Jot down some topics you wish to include in your conversation with God so that you are not speaking without thinking.

Praise: _____ _____

Repent: _____

Ask: _____

- Again today ask God to make you sensitive to the events in your daily life that give you the opportunity to show that God is first. Keep in mind the lessons you learned from Asa's life. It is easy for us to make the wrong choices as Asa did, even after years of right choices.

Yield: _____

Day 5

❏ Take Time to Reflect upon the Truth

1. Read II Corinthians 4:7-18. Check the box when you have finished reading the passage. Then answer the following questions from the passage. ❏

2. In verses 8-9 of the passage you just read, the apostle Paul speaks of the troubles he encountered in the ministry. Summarize what he is saying in these two verses.

_____

_____

_____

_____

3. Paul says in verses 16-18 that he does not faint under the weight of the trouble he has experienced and then testifies of what sustains him during troubled times. What does he say is the secret to his endurance?

_____

_____

_____

_____

4. Do you have a God-enabled endurance in the troubles of life that comes from genuinely looking "at the things which are not seen"?

_____

_____

5. If not, what would you say is keeping you from this kind of experience in your Christian life?

_____

_____

_____

6. In these verses God promises that you will have a God-enabled endurance if you are regularly seeking the things that are not seen and that are eternal. For an extended study on this topic read *Created for His Glory* by Jim Berg (Greenville, S.C.: BJU Press, 2002). It is an extended study of the realities of our great God, which the believer must know in order to be stable in times of uncertainty.

❏ Take Time to Renew Your Mind

Write Matthew 5:16 from memory.

_____

_____

_____

_____

_____

❏ Take Time to Respond to God

To build a relationship with God, you will need to respond to Him about the things you have learned from Him today. Strengthen your prayer time by "PRAYing." Jot down some topics you wish to include in your conversation with God so that you are not speaking without thinking.

Praise: _____

Repent: _____

Ask: _____

• Today make a commitment to God that you want to pursue the "things which are above" (Colossians 3:1), rather than setting so much of your attention on earthly things, so that you can have the God-enabled endurance that He wants you to have during times of trouble.

Yield: _____

❏ Take Time to Reorder Your Life

Considering this week's reflections, write below anything you need to begin to do differently in your life. List as well the person whom you will ask to hold you accountable for these changes.

_____

_____

_____

_____

Week 4

THE DELIGHT

| God Himself is always enough. |

DAY 1

❏ TAKE TIME TO READ THE TEXT

Read chapter 7, pages 61-69, of WTC.

❏ TAKE TIME TO REFLECT UPON THE TRUTH

1. In the blanks below write the two most significant statements in today's reading assignment. Be prepared to discuss why the statements you chose were significant to you.

a. _____

_____

_____

_____

_____

b. _____

_____

_____

_____

2. Your reading included the statement "When there are things that you do not know about your life's situation, you must focus on the things that you do know about your God" (WTC, 63). Think about a crisis or problem you are facing. In your own wisdom you might think that if you only had the answer to certain things related to your crisis, you could be at peace. What are those things you feel would give you peace if you knew them? _____

_____

_____

_____

_____

3. Remember the story "Courage to Face a Bully" on pages 64-65 of WTC? The relief for my daughter's unrest did not come because the bully went away but rather because she knew her father—who cared about her—was present. What does this tell you that we need to know about God for our hearts to rest?

_____

_____

❏ TAKE TIME TO RENEW YOUR MIND

Memorize Isaiah 41:10 this week. Review it daily throughout the entire week and be prepared to write it from memory on Day 5.[1]

Fear thou not; for I am with thee: be not dismayed; for I am thy God: I will strengthen thee; yea, I will help thee; yea, I will uphold thee with the right hand of my righteousness.

---

[1]If you already know Isaiah 41:10 or wish to memorize additional passsages, consider memorizing Isaiah 40:27-31, Psalm 121, or Psalm 16:8-9, 11.

❑ TAKE TIME TO RESPOND TO GOD

To build a relationship with God, you will need to respond to Him about the things you have learned from Him today. Strengthen your prayer time by "PRAYing." Jot down some topics you wish to include in your conversation with God so that you are not speaking without thinking.

Praise: _____

Repent: _____

Ask: _____

• If your spirit has been filled with worry, doubt, fears, and discouragements, you need to ask God to forgive you for your unbelief. Ask Him as well to teach you more of Himself as you meditate upon portions of His Word that acquaint you with who He is. You must spend much time inspecting His "squad car" if you are going to feel safe with Him.

Yield: _____

DAY 2

❏ TAKE TIME TO REFLECT UPON THE TRUTH

1. Read Psalm 103. Check the box when you have finished reading the passage. Then answer the following questions from the passage. ❏
2. In Psalm 103:1-2 David reminds us to give thanks to God and not to forget all His blessings—His benefits—to us. What "benefits" from God are listed in this psalm? Find ten and then put them into your own words; do not just copy down the words out of your Bible. Think through what David is saying about God and His work on our behalf.

a. _____

b. _____

c. _____

d. _____

e. _____

f. _____

g. _____

h. _____

i. _____

j. _____

❏ TAKE TIME TO RENEW YOUR MIND

Memorize Isaiah 41:10.

❏ TAKE TIME TO RESPOND TO GOD

To build a relationship with God, you will need to respond to Him about the things you have learned from Him today. Strengthen your prayer time by "PRAYing." Jot down some topics you wish to include in your conversation with God so that you are not speaking without thinking.

Praise: _____

Repent: _____

Ask: _____

_____

• Ask God to make you aware of the "benefits" He has sent your way in His goodness. Spend time praising Him for His kindness to you in these ways.

Yield: _____

DAY 3

❏ TAKE TIME TO REFLECT UPON THE TRUTH

1. Page 66 of WTC states that "God is unlimited in His power." Look up each of the references listed for that characteristic of God. In addition read Isaiah 40:9-26. Check the box when you have finished reading the passages. Then answer the following questions. ❏

2. What did you learn from these passages about the characteristics of God's power?

_____

_____

_____

3. What did you learn about God's power that should be a comfort to you when trouble comes?

_____

_____

_____

4. What sinful responses do you make in the face of trouble because you forget that God is unlimited in His power?

_____

_____

_____

❏ TAKE TIME TO RENEW YOUR MIND

Memorize Isaiah 41:10.

❏ Take Time to Respond to God

To build a relationship with God, you will need to respond to Him about the things you have learned from Him today. Strengthen your prayer time by "PRAYing." Jot down some topics you wish to include in your conversation with God so that you are not speaking without thinking.

Praise: _____

Repent: _____

Ask: _____

_____

• Ask God to show you clearly His power that He will use on your behalf to rescue you from the danger of your flesh during a crisis.

Yield: _____

DAY 4

❏ TAKE TIME TO REFLECT UPON THE TRUTH

1. Page 66 of WTC states that "God is unlimited in His wisdom." Look up each of the references listed for that characteristic of God. In addition read I Corinthians 1:23-31. Check the box when you have finished reading the passages. Then answer the following questions. ❏

2. What did you learn from these passages about the characteristics of God's wisdom?

_____

_____

_____

_____

3. What did you learn about God's wisdom that should be a comfort to you when trouble comes?

_____

_____

_____

4. What sinful responses do you make in the face of trouble because you forget that God is unlimited in His wisdom?

_____

_____

❏ TAKE TIME TO RENEW YOUR MIND

Memorize Isaiah 41:10.

❏ TAKE TIME TO RESPOND TO GOD

To build a relationship with God, you will need to respond to Him about the things you have learned from Him today. Strengthen your prayer time by "PRAYing." Jot down some topics you wish to include in your conversation with God so that you are not speaking without thinking.

Praise: _____

Repent: _____

Ask: _____

- Ask God to show you clearly His wisdom that He will use on your behalf to rescue you from the danger of your flesh during a crisis.

Yield: _____

DAY 5

❏ TAKE TIME TO REFLECT UPON THE TRUTH

1. Page 66 of WTC states that "God is unlimited in His love." Look up each of the references listed for that characteristic of God. In addition read Romans 8:31-39 again—you read it in an earlier lesson too. Check the box when you have finished reading the passages. Then answer the following questions from what you have read. ❏

2. What did you learn from these passages about the characteristics of God's love?

   _____

   _____

   _____

   _____

3. What did you learn—or were you reminded of—about God's love that should be a comfort to you when trouble comes?

   _____

   _____

   _____

   _____

4. What sinful responses do you make in the face of trouble because you forget that God is unlimited in His love for you?

   _____

   _____

   _____

❏ Take Time to Renew Your Mind

Write Isaiah 41:10 from memory.

_____

_____

_____

_____

❏ Take Time to Respond to God

To build a relationship with God, you will need to respond to Him about the things you have learned from Him today. Strengthen your prayer time by "PRAYing." Jot down some topics you wish to include in your conversation with God so that you are not speaking without thinking.

<u>P</u>raise: _____

<u>R</u>epent: _____

<u>A</u>sk: _____

• Ask God to show you clearly His love that He will use on your behalf to rescue you from the danger of your flesh during a crisis.

<u>Y</u>ield: _____

❏ Take Time to Reorder Your Life

Considering this week's reflections, write below anything you need to begin to do differently in your life. List as well the person whom you will ask to hold you accountable for these changes.

_____

_____

_____

_____